UNIT 15

On the Move

INTER·ACTIVE

Mathematics

Activities & Investigations

GLENCOE

McGraw-Hill

New York, New York   Columbus, Ohio   Mission Hills, California   Peoria, Illinois

Send all inquiries to:
Glencoe/McGraw-Hill
936 Eastwind Drive
Westerville, OH 43081

ISBN: 0-02-824517-2 (Student Resource Book)
ISBN: 0-02-824499-0 (Teacher's Edition)

2 3 4 5 6 7 8 9 10 VH/LH-P 01 00 99 98 97 96 95 94

CONTENTS

UNIT 15

ON THE MOVE
GRAPHING AND FUNCTIONS

Interdisciplinary Applications

DAVID FOSTER

"The national goal is to develop mathematical power for all students. My vision for learning mathematics includes a student-oriented classroom culture, where students are taking charge of their own learning and are actively engaged in a curriculum that reflects today's world, not the mathematics of 150 years ago."

**Former Teaching Consultant
Middle Grades Mathematics
Renaissance
Morgan Hill, California**
Author of Units 1, 2, 5, 6, 7, 8, 10, 11, 13, 15, 16, 17, and 18

David Foster received his B.A. in mathematics from San Diego State University and has taken graduate courses in computer science at San Jose State University. He has taught mathematics and computer science for nineteen years at the middle school, high school, and college level. Mr. Foster is a founding member of the California Mathematics Project Advisory Committee and was Co-Director of the Santa Clara Valley Mathematics Project. Most recently, he has taken the position of Consulting Author for Glencoe Publishing. Mr. Foster is a member of many professional organizations including the National Council of Teachers of Mathematics and regularly conducts in-service workshops for teachers. He is also the author of a book on computer science.

SANDIE GILLIAM

"Many students only see mathematics as isolated number facts and formulas to memorize. By using this program, which incorporates the mathematics into a context of large, real-life units tied together with literature, science, and history, the middle school student can find meaning in the mathematics."

**Mathematics Teacher
San Lorenzo Valley High School
Felton, California**
Co-author of Unit 14

Sandie Gilliam received her B.A. from San Jose State University and is a mentor teacher and instructor for the Monterey Bay Area Mathematics Project. She was a semi-finalist for the Presidential Award for Excellence in the Teaching of Mathematics in the state of California. Ms. Gilliam has served as a consultant for the California Department of Education and many local school districts and county offices of education. She is a member of the National Council of Teachers of Mathematics and is a frequent speaker at conferences and teacher in-service workshops. Ms. Gilliam was a writer and consultant for Glencoe's *Investigating Mathematics: An Interactive Approach.*

JACK PRICE

"This program is designed to help students become mathematically powerful as they develop problem-solving skills and self-reliance, as well as the ability to work well with others. At the same time, they will strengthen their basic skills and be exposed to new and exciting ideas in mathematics."

**Co-Director, Center for Science
and Mathematics Education
California State Polytechnic
University
Pomona, California**
Author of Unit 3

Jack Price received his B.A. from Eastern Michigan University and his Doctorate in Mathematics Education from Wayne State University. Dr. Price has been active in mathematics education for over 40 years, 38 of those years at grades K through 12. In his current position, he teaches mathematics and methods courses for preservice teachers and consults with school districts on curriculum change. He is president of the National Council of Teachers of Mathematics, is a frequent speaker at professional conferences, conducts many teacher in-service workshops, and is an author of numerous mathematics instructional materials.

INTERACTIVE MATHEMATICS AUTHORS

KAY McCLAIN

"Building conceptual understanding in mathematics challenges us to re-define what it means to know and do mathematics. This program was developed to allow teachers to become facilitators of learning while students explore and investigate mathematics — strengthening their understanding and stimulating interest."

Kay McClain

**Doctoral Candidate
George Peabody College
Vanderbilt University
Nashville, Tennessee**
Author of Unit 9, Co-author of Unit 14

Kay McClain received her B.A. from Auburn University and her Educational Specialist degree from the University of Montevallo in Montevallo, Alabama. While a teacher at Mountain Brook Middle School in Birmingham, she received the Presidential Award for Excellence in the Teaching of Mathematics in the state of Alabama. Ms. McClain is a Woodrow Wilson fellow and a member of the National Council of Teachers of Mathematics. She regularly conducts teacher in-service workshops and is a frequent speaker at local, state, and national mathematics education conferences. She is also an author of middle school mathematics instructional materials.

BARNEY MARTINEZ

"Students learn mathematics best when their teacher enables them to become actively involved in worthwhile mathematical investigations. Students should be encouraged to interact with each other. Then, through their collaborative efforts, students build their own understanding of mathematics."

Barney Martinez

**Mathematics Teacher
Jefferson High School
Daly City, California**
Co-Author of Unit 12

Barney Martinez received his B.S. in mathematics from The University of San Francisco and is an instructor of pre-service mathematics teachers at the College of Notre Dame in Belmont, California. Mr. Martinez currently serves on the Mathematics Development Team of the California Department of Education and the Pursuing Excellence Revision Advisory Committee. He is a member of the National Council of Teachers of Mathematics and is very active as a speaker and workshop leader at professional development conferences.

LINDA DRITSAS

"This program is designed to encourage students to be creative and inventive, while gaining mathematical power. Open-ended situations and investigations provide the setting that allows students to work at varying depths, while nurturing their natural curiosity to learn."

Linda Dritsas

**Mathematics Coordinator
Fresno Unified School District
Fresno, California**
Author of Unit 4, Co-author of Unit 12

Linda Dritsas received her B.A. and M.A. from California State University at Fresno. She taught middle school mathematics for many years and, for two years, taught mathematics at California State University at Fresno. Ms. Dritsas has been the Central Section President of the California Mathematics Council and is a member of the National Council of Teachers of Mathematics and the Association for Supervision and Curriculum Development. She frequently conducts mathematics teacher in-service workshops and is an author of numerous mathematics instructional materials, including those for middle school students and teachers.

Each of the Consultants read all 18 units while each Reviewer read one unit. The Consultants and Reviewers gave suggestions for improving the Student Resource Books, Teacher's Editions, Cooperative Group Cards, Posters, and Transparencies. The Writers wrote the Student Diversity Strategies that appear in the Teacher's Edition.

CONSULTANTS

Dr. Judith Jacobs, *Units 1-18*
Director, Center for Science
and Mathematics Education
California State
Polytechnic University
Pomona, California

Dr. Cleo M. Meek, *Units 1-18*
Mathematics Consultant,
Retired
North Carolina Dept. of
Public Instruction
Raleigh, North Carolina

Beatrice Moore-Harris,
Units 1-18
College Board Equity 2000
Site Coordinator
Fort Worth Independent
School District
Fort Worth, Texas

Deborah J. Murphy, *Units 1-18*
Mathematics Teacher
Killingsworth Jr. High School,
ABC Unified School District
Cerritos, California

Javier Solorzano, *Units 1-18*
Mathematics Teacher
South El Monte High School
South El Monte, California

WRITERS

Student Diversity
Teacher's Edition

Dr. Gilbert J. Cuevas
Professor of Mathematics
Education
University of Miami
Coral Gables, Florida

Sally C. Mayberry, *Ed.D.*
Assistant Professor
Mathematics/Science
Education
St. Thomas University
Miami, Florida

REVIEWERS

John W. Anson, *Unit 11*
Mathematics Teacher
Arroyo Seco Junior High
School
Valencia, California

Laura Beckwith, *Unit 13*
Mathematics Department
Chairperson
William James Middle School
Fort Worth, Texas

Betsy C. Blume, *Unit 6*
Vice Principal/
Director of Curriculum
Valleyview Middle School
Denville, New Jersey

James F. Bohan, *Unit 11*
Mathematics K-12 Program
Coordinator
Manheim Township School
District
Lancaster, Pennsylvania

Dr. Carol Fry Bohlin, *Unit 14*
Director, San Joaquin Valley
Mathematics Project
Associate Professor,
Mathematics Education
California State University,
Fresno
Fresno, California

David S. Bradley, *Unit 9*
Mathematics
Teacher/Department
Chairperson
Jefferson Jr. High
Kearns, Utah

Dr. Diane Briars, *Unit 9*
Mathematics Specialist
Pittsburgh City Schools
Pittsburgh, Pennsylvania

Jackie Britton, *Unit 18*
Mathematics Teacher
V. W. Miller Intermediate
Pasadena, Texas

Sybil Y. Brown, *Unit 8*
Mathematics Teacher
Franklin Alternative Middle
School
Columbus, Ohio

Blanche Smith Brownley, *Unit 18*
Supervising Director of
Mathematics (Acting)
District of Columbia Public
Schools
Washington, D.C.

Bruce A. Camblin, *Unit 7*
Mathematics Teacher
Weld School District 6
Greeley, Colorado

Cleo Campbell, *Unit 15*
Coordinator of Mathematics,
K-12
Anne Arundel County
Public Schools
Annapolis, Maryland

Savas Carabases, *Unit 13*
Mathematics Supervisor
Camden City School District
Camden City, New Jersey

W. Karla Castello, *Unit 6*
Mathematics Teacher
Yerba Buena High School
San Jose, California

Diane M. Chase, *Unit 16*
Mathematics Teacher/
Department Chairperson
Pacific Jr. High School
Vancouver, Washington

Dr. Phyllis Zweig Chinn, *Unit 9*
Professor of Mathematics
Humboldt State University
Arcata, California

Nancy W. Crowther, *Unit 17*
Mathematics Teacher
Sandy Springs Middle School
Atlanta, Georgia

Regina F. Cullen, *Unit 13*
Supervisor of Mathematics
West Essex Regional Schools
North Caldwell, New Jersey

Sara J. Danielson, *Unit 17*
Mathematics Teacher
Albany Middle School
Albany, California

Lorna Denman, *Unit 10*
Mathematics Teacher
Sunny Brae Middle School
Arcata, California

Richard F. Dube, *Unit 4*
Mathematics Supervisor
Taunton High School
Taunton, Massachusetts

Mary J. Dubsky, *Unit 1*
Mathematics Curriculum
Specialist
Baltimore City Public Schools
Baltimore, Maryland

Dr. Leo Edwards, *Unit 5*
Director, Mathematics/
Science Education Center
Fayetteville State University
Fayetteville, North Carolina

Connie Fairbanks, *Unit 7*
Mathematics Teacher
South Whittier Intermediate
School
Whittier, California

Ana Marina C. Gomezgil, *Unit 15*
District Translator/Interpreter
Sweetwater Union
High School District
Chula Vista, California

Sandy R. Guerra, *Unit 9*
Mathematics Teacher
Harry H. Rogers Middle
School
San Antonio, Texas

Rick Hall, *Unit 4*
Curriculum Coordinator
San Bernardino County
Superintendent of Schools
San Bernardino, California

Carolyn Hansen, *Unit 14*
Instructional Specialist
Williamsville Central Schools
Williamsville, New York

Jenny Hembree, *Unit 8*
Mathematics Teacher
Shelby Co. East Middle
School
Shelbyville, Kentucky

Susan Hertz, *Unit 16*
Mathematics Teacher
Paul Revere Middle School
Houston, Texas

Janet L. Hollister, *Unit 5*
Mathematics Teacher
LaCumbre Middle School
Santa Barbara, California

Dorothy Nachtigall Hren, *Unit 12*
Mathematics Teacher/
Department Chairperson
Northside Middle School
Norfolk, Virginia

Grace Hutchings, *Unit 3*
Mathematics Teacher
Parkman Middle School
Woodland Hills, California

Lyle D. Jensen, *Unit 18*
Mathematics Teacher
Albright Middle School
Villa Park, Illinois

Robert R. Jones, *Unit 7*
Chief Consultant,
  Mathematics, Retired
North Carolina Department
  of Public Instruction
Raleigh, North Carolina

Mary Kay Karl, *Unit 3*
Mathematics Coordinator
Community Consolidated
  School District 54
Schaumburg, Illinois

Janet King, *Unit 14*
Mathematics Teacher
North Gulfport Junior High
Gulfport, Mississippi

Franca Koeller, *Unit 17*
Mathematics Mentor Teacher
Arroyo Seco Junior High
  School
Valencia, California

Louis La Mastro, *Unit 2*
Mathematics/Computer
  Science Teacher
North Bergen High School
North Bergen, New Jersey

Patrick Lamberti, *Unit 6*
Supervisor of Mathematics
Toms River Schools
Toms River, New Jersey

Dr. Betty Larkin, *Unit 14*
Mathematics Coordinator
  K - 12
Lee County School District
Fort Myers, Florida

Ann Lawrence, *Unit 1*
Mathematics
  Teacher/Department
  Coordinator
Mountain Brook Jr. High
  School
Mountain Brook, Alabama

Catherine Louise Marascalco,
  Unit 3
Mathematics Teacher
Southaven Elementary
  School
Southaven, Mississippi

Dr. Hannah Masterson, *Unit 10*
Mathematics Specialist
Suffolk Board of
  Cooperative Education
Dix Hills, New York

Betty Monroe Nelson, *Unit 8*
Mathematics Teacher
Blackburn Middle School
Jackson, Mississippi

Dale R. Oliver, *Unit 2*
Assistant Professor of
  Mathematics
Humboldt State University
Arcata, California

Carol A. Pudlin, *Unit 4*
Mathematics Teacher/
  Consultant
Griffiths Middle School
Downey, California

Diane Duggento Sawyer,
  Unit 15
Mathematics Chairperson
Exeter Area Junior High
Exeter, New Hampshire

Donald W. Scheuer, Jr., *Unit 12*
Mathematics Department
  Chairperson
Abington Junior High
Abington, Pennsylvania

Linda S. Shippey, *Unit 8*
Mathematics Teacher
Bondy Intermediate School
Pasadena, Texas

Barbara Smith, *Unit 1*
Mathematics Supervisor,
  K-12
Unionville-Chadds Ford
  School District
Kennett Square, Pennsylvania

Stephanie Z. Smith, *Unit 14*
Project Assistant
University of Wisconsin-
  Madison
Madison, Wisconsin

Dora M. Swart, *Unit 11*
Mathematics Teacher
W. F. West High School
Chehalis, Washington

Ciro J. Tacinelli, Sr., *Unit 8*
Curriculum Director:
  Mathematics
Hamden Public Schools
Hamden, Connecticut

Kathy L. Terwelp, *Unit 12*
K-8 Mathematics Supervisor
Summit Public Schools
Summit, New Jersey

Marty Terzieff, *Unit 18*
Secondary Math Curriculum
  Chairperson
Mead Junior High School
Mead, Washington

Linda L. Walker, *Unit 18*
Mathematics Teacher
Cobb Middle School
Tallahassee, Florida

ON THE MOVE

Looking Ahead

In this unit, you will see how mathematics can be used to answer questions about motion and change. You will experience:

▶ using graphs and maps to communicate information

▶ recording data and constructing graphs of the data

▶ determining speed and distance

▶ determining acceleration and deceleration

▶ analyzing data using graphs

Did You Ever Wonder?

What do mathematics and cars have to do with each other? Turn the page to see how Stephen Lovett of Reston, Virginia, combines the two.

Teens in the News

Featuring: Stephen A. Lovett
Age: 17
Hometown: Reston, Virginia
Career Goal: Chief Executive Officer of Chrysler Corporation
Interests: Water sports, community service projects

Several years ago while Stephen Lovett was mowing a neighbor's grass, he noticed that their car was really dirty. He offered to wash and wax it. Stephen really got carried away, and before he knew it, he had completely cleaned and detailed the car!

Word quickly got around the neighborhood about what a great job Stephen had done on the car. Neighbors started calling Stephen and asking him to clean their cars. So, at age 13, Stephen started Lovett Enterprises. He specializes in providing detailing services, such as thorough vacuuming of carpets and cloth upholstery, glass cleaning, and wheel and tire cleaning at a fraction of the cost that professional car detailers charge.

Business grew, and Stephen created a franchise agreement. He supplies four other teens with all the materials and supplies that they need to do car detailing. These teens agree to operate under the name Lovett Enterprises. In return, each teen pays Stephen a percentage of the business he or she conducts each month.

Stephen uses a computer and a software program to do all of the accounting for Lovett Enterprises. He keeps track of the money he earns and the money his franchises earn.

Stephen pays a lot of attention to his customers. He sends every customer a thank-you note and he leaves candy in their car when they come to pick it up. At Lovett Enterprises, the difference really is in the details!

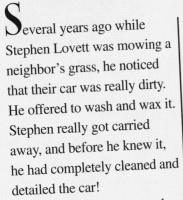

Retail price; $9,845
Cost of all parts purchased separately; $38,652

SUM OF THE PARTS

Buying a car piece by piece would cost considerably more than buying the assembled car. Consider the 1990 Ford Escort LX.

Team Project

How Slow Must You Go?

Stephen can make a car shine like a dime. But no one can make a car stop on a dime. The *total stopping distance* depends on the speed of the car, the thinking distance, and the braking distance.

Find out what is meant by *thinking distance* and *braking distance.* Use the information in the chart to make three graphs comparing the thinking distance, braking distance, and total stopping distance with its original speed. Use your graphs to predict the total stopping distance for a car going 65 miles per hour. The State Highway Patrol recommends that for every 10 mph of speed you keep one car length between you and the car in front of you. Does that seem reasonable? Explain why or why not.

Original Speed (mph)	Thinking Distance (ft)	Braking Distance (ft)	Total Stopping Distance (ft)
15	16	12	28
25	27	34	61
35	38	67	105
45	49	111	160
55	60	165	225

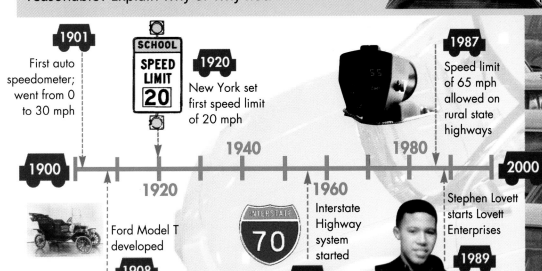

1901 First auto speedometer; went from 0 to 30 mph

SCHOOL SPEED LIMIT 20

1920 New York set first speed limit of 20 mph

1987 Speed limit of 65 mph allowed on rural state highways

1900

1920

1940

1980

2000

1960 Interstate Highway system started

Stephen Lovett starts Lovett Enterprises

1989

Ford Model T developed

1908

INTERSTATE 70

1956

For more information

If you would like more information about starting your own business, contact:

FUTURE BUSINESS LEADERS OF AMERICA 1908 Association Drive Reston, Virginia 22091

You can learn more about the math Stephen uses in his business by completing the activities in this unit.

Setting the Scene

MATHEMATICS TOOLKIT

Many professions require the use of tools. This mathematics toolkit includes tools you may find useful as you study this unit. At times you may feel lost or not know where to begin when presented with a problem situation. You should take time to review this toolkit to see how the characters in the script used mathematics to solve their problem.

Narrator: Hector, Amber, and Mi-Ling are friends having lunch at their middle school. It's the first day back after the winter break.

Hector: So what kinds of presents did you guys get over the holidays?

Mi-Ling: I got some new outfits. In fact, I'm wearing one now. How do you like it?

Amber: You look great!

Hector: Simply stunning, darling. How about giving us a fashion show?

Mi-Ling: Okay, get real. So what did *you* get, Hector? A roll of quarters for the arcade?

Hector: Hey, lay off. So, I like to play video games, okay? I like the action and the speed.

Amber: That reminds me. My little brother Ryan got one of those Speed Track sets for Christmas. You know, those miniature cars that race around the track.

Hector: Yeah. On TV, they say those cars are "faster than real life."

Mi-Ling: Are you serious? Something that small can't travel that fast, can it? I don't think, those little cars can go faster than a regular car.

Amber: I don't know. When you see those little cars shoot around that track, they sure look fast. How can you tell?

Hector: I think it's just a gimmick. You know, just to get you to buy it.

Mi-Ling: They can't do that. Aren't there, like, truth in advertising laws?

Amber: I don't know, but I'll bet there's a way to find out.

Hector: Yeah! Maybe we can sue them for false advertising and make a million bucks!

Amber: You watch way too much TV, Hector. Anyway, how can we do this?

Mi-Ling: Well, tell us about the set.

Amber: Okay. The track is set up in an oval shape. At each end, there are three curved pieces. The sides of the track are made of straight pieces. The track is designed for two cars. In each straightaway, the cars cross over and change position. Let me draw you a picture.

Mi-Ling: That gives me an idea. I think I know how to figure out how fast the cars really go. Can we come over to your house after school and "test drive" my idea?

Amber: Very funny. Sure, that would be cool.

Hector: Maybe we'll be able to write to one of those consumer shows and tell them about our case. We could be famous!

Stop the Script!
Determine how you could find the speed of the miniature cars.

Narrator: The friends meet at Amber's house after school.

Amber: Okay, so here it is. I asked Ryan if we could use it, and he said okay, but I had to give him a dollar!

Hector: Hey, this is pretty cool! Almost as cool as video games, but not quite. So, Mi-Ling, what's this hot idea?

Mi-Ling: Okay. We can find the speed by timing the cars as they go around the track.

Amber: That's it? Won't that just give us their time in seconds?

Hector: Yeah. We need to know the speed in miles per hour, not seconds.

Mi-Ling: I know. We can calculate speed by dividing the distance by the time. But first, we need to convert seconds to minutes and minutes to hours. We'll just use a calculator.

Hector: I don't get it— you're gonna have to show me.

Mi-Ling: I have a stopwatch. Hector, you start the cars.

Hector: Okay.

Mi-Ling: Amber, you take the stopwatch and time the car for exactly one lap around the track. Start the watch when the car is here and then stop it when the car comes back to the same exact place on the track. We'll do this at least four or five times.

Narrator: They timed the miniature car five times as it went around the track. The car's times are shown below.

Lap	Time (seconds)
1	4.18
2	3.21
3	3.20
4	3.18
5	3.22

Hector: Now that we've got these times, how do we find an average time?

Amber: Well, it looks like I messed up timing the first one and three of them are almost the same. Why don't we use 3.21 seconds as the average time?

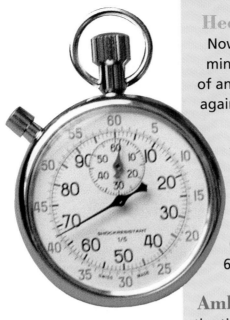

Mi-Ling: That makes sense. Okay, now let's convert the number of seconds to hours.

Amber: Wait a minute— 3.21 seconds isn't even close to an hour!

Mi-Ling: Right. We need to find out what part of an hour it is. We can do that by first changing the number of seconds to parts of a minute. So, divide 3.21 by 60, since there are 60 seconds in a minute.

Amber: I get 0.053508.

Mi-Ling: That's 0.053508 *minutes*.

Hector: Hey, I get it. Now we need to turn this minute number into parts of an hour. So we divide again by 60.

Amber: Because there are 60 minutes in an hour?

Hector: Yeah. 0.053508 divided by 60 is 0.0008918 *hours*.

Amber: Okay, we've got the time in parts of an hour, but what about the speed?

Mi-Ling: You can find the speed by finding the distance the car traveled and dividing by the time. You know, miles per hour means miles divided by hours. Like if you drove 100 miles and it took 2 hours, how fast did you go?

Hector: That's easy—50 miles an hour. You just divide 100 by 2.

Amber: So how are we going to find the distance?

Hector: Well, just look at the track. There are four straight pieces on each side and three curved pieces at each end. If we measure the two kinds of pieces, then we can find the total distance.

Mi-Ling: That works great for the straight track, but what about the curves?

Amber: I think I know how to measure the curve. If you put the two ends together, you get a circle. You can find the distance around a circle, or the **circumference**, by multiplying the distance across the circle, called the **diameter**, by 3.14. Don't you guys remember this stuff?

Hector: Oh, yeah. We learned that stuff last year in math class. Okay, a straight piece is about 7 inches long. So, 7 inches times 8 straight pieces of track is 56 inches.

Amber: Okay. For the curves, I can measure across the race track from the center of one straightaway to the center of the other. I get $18\frac{3}{4}$ inches.

Hector: If I multiply 18.75 inches times 3.14 on my calculator, I get...58.875 inches. So the total track is 56 + 58.875 or...114.875 inches long.

Mi-Ling: Now we need to convert 114.875 inches to miles. Let's start by rounding 114.875 to 115. That will make our calculations a little easier.

Amber: We can do the same thing with inches that we did with seconds. We'll need to convert 115 inches to feet, and then to miles.

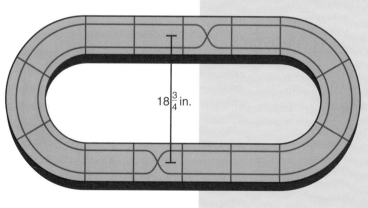

$18\frac{3}{4}$ in.

Mi-Ling: You're right. There are 12 inches in a foot and 5,280 feet in a mile.

Amber: So we divide 115 by 12 inches and get 9.583333 feet.

Hector: Now divide 9.583333 by 5,280. What did you get?

Amber: 0.001815 miles.

Hector: Hey, wait a minute. That's so small! Does this really work?

Amber: Sure! Remember that we also got a small number for the time. It was 0.0008918 hours.

Mi-Ling: Since speed is distance divided by time, let's divide 0.001815 miles by 0.0008918 hours.

Amber: I get 2.0352. Wow, the car only goes about 2 miles an hour!

Hector: What a ripoff! Two miles an hour is top speed for a real-life car. NOT!

Amber: Let's write to that consumer show.

Hector: Yeah, we'll be famous.

Mi-Ling: Hey, this was pretty cool.

This concludes the Mathematics Toolkit. It included many mathematical tools for you to use throughout the unit. As you work through this unit, you should use these tools to help you solve problems. You may want to explain how to use these mathematical tools in your journal. Or you may want to create a toolkit notebook and add the mathematical tools you discover throughout this unit.

On the Road

A class from Pleasanton Middle School went on a field trip to the Monterey Bay Aquarium on Cannery Row in Monterey, California. The map and graph below illustrate the bus trip from Pleasanton to Monterey.

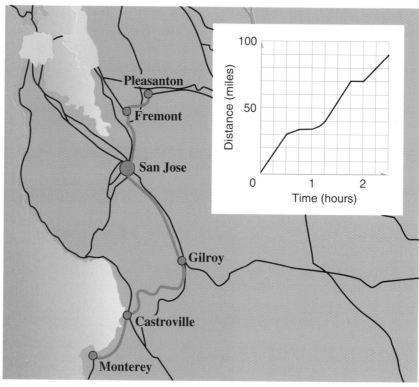

Describe the trip, making use of the graph and the map. It will be easier if you describe the trip in sections. Be sure to include the speed of the bus in your description. Be prepared to present your findings to the class.

THE OLYMPIAD

MENU station

A

One-Legged Hop Race

In this activity, each person in the group will race against time. Choose one person to be the starter and another person to be the timer.

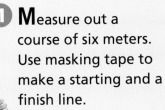

1 **M**easure out a course of six meters. Use masking tape to make a starting and a finish line.

2 **A**t the starter's signal, one member of the group hops on one leg over the six-meter course.

3 **R**ecord the time that it took the person to hop the length of the course.

4 **R**epeat the race, rotating the positions of starter and timer, until each member of the group has raced.

5 **C**onstruct a graph of your group's performance. Let one axis represent the distance and let the other axis represent the time in which each racer finishes. Plot a point on the graph showing the time and distance for each racer. Then draw a separate line from the origin to each point. Label each line with the racer's name.

MENU station B

TWO-LEGGED HOP RACE

In this activity, each person in the group will race for distance. Choose one person to be the spotter and another person to be the timer.

1 **U**se masking tape to make a starting line.

2 **A**t the timer's signal, one member of the group hops on two legs as far as he or she can go in six seconds. The timer calls out the seconds as they pass ("1, 2, 3,...").

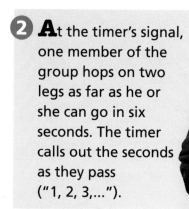

3 **T**he spotter locates where the racer was when the timer yelled "6." The distance the racer was from the starting line is measured and recorded.

5 **C**onstruct a graph of your group's performance. Let one axis represent the distance and let the other axis represent the time in which each racer finishes. Plot a point on the graph showing the time and distance for each racer. Then draw a separate line from the origin to each point. Label each line with the racer's name.

4 **R**epeat the race, rotating the positions of spotter and timer, until each member of the group has raced.

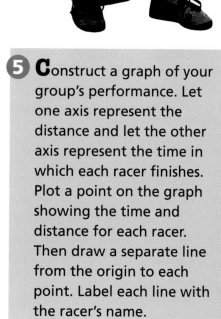

Relay Race

In this activity, the members of the group will run a relay race. Choose one person to be the timer.

1 Use masking tape to make a starting line. Five meters from the starting line, make a second line. Five meters from the second line, make a third line. Five meters from the third line, make a finish line.

2 Set up a relay race with three racers, with a racer on each line. On the timer's signal, the first racer begins by walking heel-toe, heel-toe. The timer calls out the seconds as they pass ("1, 2, 3,..."). When the first racer reaches and tags the second racer, the first racer listens for his or her time. The same thing happens with each racer. The timer stops the watch when the third racer crosses the finish line.

3 All three times are recorded.

4 Run the relay again, this time with another person as the timer.

5 Construct a graph of your group's two races on the same set of axes. Let one axis represent the distance and let the other axis represent the time in which each racer finishes. Plot a point on the graph showing the time and distance for each racer. Then draw lines from the origin to the first racer's time, from the first racer's time to the second racer's time, and from the second racer's time to the third racer's time. You may want to use different colors for the two races.

MENU
station

SHUTTLE RACE

In this activity, each member of the group will run a shuttle race. Choose one person to be the timer and another to be the recorder.

1 **U**se masking tape to make a starting line. Five meters from the starting line, make a second line.

2 **I**n this shuttle race, the racers race back and forth four times between the two marks, ending at the starting line. On the timer's signal, the racer walks *forward* heel-toe, heel-toe. On the way back, the racer walks *backward* heel-toe, heel-toe. Then the process is repeated. The timer calls out the seconds as they pass ("1, 2, 3,...").

3 **T**he recorder notes the times that the racer touches each line and crosses the finish line. Thus, four times should be recorded for each race.

5 **C**onstruct a graph of each racer's performance. Let one axis represent the distance and let the other axis represent the times at which each racer touched each line. Plot a point on the graph for each of the four times. Then draw a line from the origin to the first point, from the first point to the second, from the second to the third, and from the third to the fourth.

4 **R**epeat the race, rotating the positions of timer and recorder, until each member of the group has raced.

MEDLEY RACE

In this activity, the members of the group will run a medley race. A medley race requires a number of different types of racing styles. Choose one person to be the timer.

1 **U**se masking tape to make a starting line. Five meters from the starting line, make a second line; eight meters from the second line, make a third line; ten meters from the third line, make a finish line.

2 **S**et up a relay race with three racers, with a racer on each line. On the timer's signal, the first racer begins by hopping on one foot. The timer calls out the seconds as they pass ("1, 2, 3,..."). When the first racer reaches and tags the second racer, the first racer listens for his or her time. When tagged by the first racer, the second racer begins walking heel-toe, heel-toe and listens for his or her time. When tagged by the second racer, the third racer begins hopping on two feet.

3 **A**ll three times are recorded.

4 **R**un the relay again, this time with another person as the timer.

5 **C**onstruct a graph of your group's two races on the same set of axes. Let one axis represent the distance and let the other axis represent the time in which each racer finishes. Plot a point on the graph showing the time and distance for each racer. Then draw lines from the origin to the first racer's time, from the first racer's time to the second racer's time, and from the second racer's time to the third racer's time. You may want to use different colors for the two races.

Once Upon a Time ...

Each graph below shows the distance an object moves over a certain time period. Interpret each graph and create a story for each that explains the movement of the object.

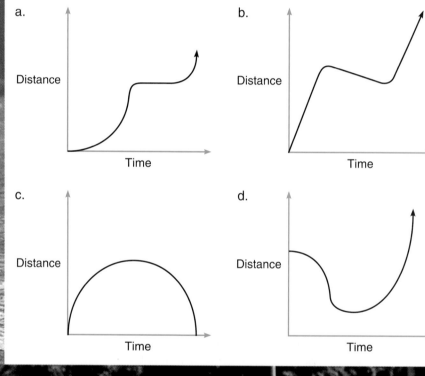

a.

Distance

Time

b.

Distance

Time

c.

Distance

Time

d.

Distance

Time

A Day at the Races

The graph below illustrates a six-furlong horse race involving four horses. The names of the horses are shown on the graph. Imagine that you are the race announcer. Describe the race as you would announce it at a race track. Be sure to write exactly what you would say as the announcer.

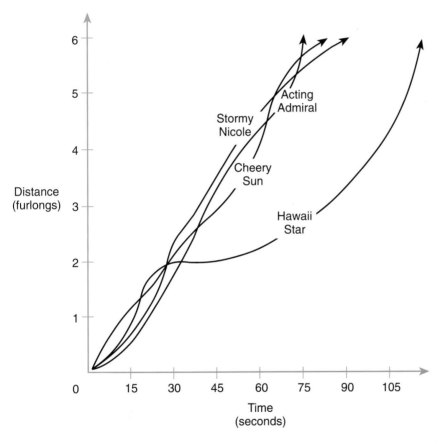

3-2-1 BLAST OFF!

You are a NASA engineer at Mission Control. Your job is to analyze the launch of a space shuttle. From your analysis, adjustments can be made for future shuttle missions. Your analysis will take the form of an oral presentation to your supervisors on the speed and **acceleration**, or the rate of change in speed, of the space shuttle during the launch.

In order to do your analysis, you will use data from the launch of a space shuttle. This data is provided in the Data Bank. Use the data to sketch a graph or series of graphs that describe the flight. Calculate the average speed of the shuttle and illustrate intervals of acceleration and speed on your graph(s).

Plan and give an oral group presentation. Use poster board to display your graphs, illustrations, charts, or other findings. Explain the characteristics of the launch and how they are illustrated through the graphs that you drew.

The Speeding Ticket

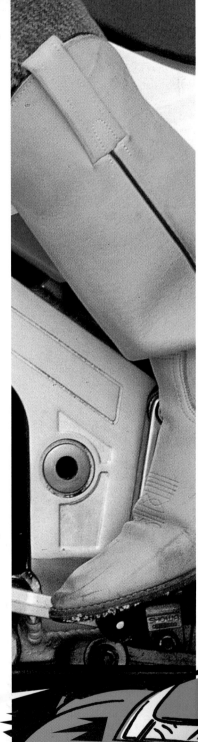

You are a highway patrol officer, seated on a motorcycle, on a curvy section of Highway 1. The posted speed limit is 45 miles per hour (mph) on this stretch of highway. You are monitoring traffic with a radar gun. The first exit is 3.6 miles up the road. Your radar picks up a speeding car averaging 68 mph. When you try to start your motorcycle to follow the car, it won't start. You try again and again, and soon you fear that you won't be able to catch the speeding car before it can turn off the highway. Finally, your motorcycle starts and you begin your pursuit 30 seconds after the speeding car has passed you on the roadside.

How fast do you need to go to catch up to the speeding car? What is your average speed in pursuit? How fast do you need to accelerate? Is your own speed reasonable and safe? Explain why this is or is not a good location at which to monitor traffic. Illustrate the speed of the speeding car as well as your own motorcycle during this pursuit. Be prepared to share your findings with the class.

SPEED LIMIT 45

How Far, How Fast?

Speed Racer

Place one end of a board measuring at least 2 meters atop two books, making a ramp. Mark a starting line on the top end of the ramp with masking tape. Let a toy car go at the starting line and clock how long it takes for the car to come to a complete stop. Measure the distance that the car traveled.

Repeat the process, changing the height of the ramp from two books to four books, then six books, and finally, eight books. Sketch two sets of graphs. Compare the distances traveled to the heights of the ramps and compare the average speeds of the cars to the heights of the ramps. Analyze your results and write about your findings

What a Drip!

Place one end of a 2-meter board atop two books, making a ramp with the starting line at the top end of the ramp. Make a small hole in the center of a coffee can and fill it with water. Let the coffee can go at the starting line with the hole at the bottom, touching the board. As the coffee can rolls down the ramp, a spot will appear at each revolution of the coffee can. When the coffee can gets to the bottom of the ramp, let it roll until it comes to a complete stop. Measure the distances of each water spot from the starting line. Make sure that you measure from the top of each dot, as some dots may run.

Repeat the process, changing the height of the ramp from two books to four books, then six books, and finally, eight books. Sketch a set of graphs comparing the distances of each dot from the starting line to the number of books. Analyze your results and write about your findings.

Speed it Up!

Choose a timer and two spotters. Place one end of a 2-meter board atop two books, making a ramp with the starting line at the top end of the ramp. Use masking tape to mark off lines on the board every 50 cm. Also mark off 50-cm intervals on the floor from the end of the board until you have marked 2 meters on the floor. Let a toy car go at the starting line. As the car rolls down the ramp, the timer calls out the seconds ("1, 2, 3,..."). The spotters determine the time that the car crosses each mark as it comes down the ramp.

Repeat the process, changing the height of the ramp from two books to four books, then six books, and finally, eight books. Sketch a set of graphs comparing the time of the car with each of the distances. Analyze your results and write about your findings.

Up and Down

Choose a timer and two spotters. Place one end of a board measuring 2 meters atop four books, making a downward ramp. Then place one end of a board measuring 3 meters against the end of the 2-meter board that is on the floor and place the other end atop four books, making an upward ramp. Mark a starting line on the top end of the 2-meter ramp with masking tape. Then mark off lines on the board every 50 cm down the 2-meter ramp and up the 3-meter ramp. Let a toy car go at the starting line. As the car rolls down the ramp, the timer calls out the seconds ("1, 2, 3,..."). The spotters determine the time that the car crossed each mark as it goes down and up the ramps. Note the point at which the car begins to travel backward down the ramp or note that the car went off the edge of the 3-meter ramp.

Repeat the process, changing the height of the ramps from four books to six books and then eight books. Sketch a set of graphs comparing the time of the car with each of the distances. Analyze your results and write about your findings.

A Thrill a Minute

At amusement parks there are a variety of rides in which visitors experience different types of motion. In this activity, you will read about five different ride situations. Read and analyze each situation. Work in your groups to determine the paths, speeds, times, and distances each of the rides take. Sketch graphs of the movement of the objects in the rides. These graphs may be drawn in relationship to distance and time, speed and time, or speed and distance. Then explain how the graph illustrates the speed of the objects and where the objects accelerate, decelerate, or stay at a constant speed. Be prepared to present your analysis to the class.

The Log Ride

You enter a log on a slowly moving turntable. When all have boarded, the log moves in a slow, steady motion to the base of an incline. The log slows almost to a stop as it starts up the incline. The motion is constant as the log climbs the incline on a conveyor belt. At the top of the incline, the log accelerates slowly, building speed as it proceeds to a waterfall. The log speeds down the waterfall and plunges into a pool below, creating a huge splash and nearly stopping the log's forward momentum. The log slowly flows to the end of the ride. You exit the ride where it began as it moves around the turntable again.

The Bumper Cars

Your bumper car ride begins with the car having no power. At the sound of the bell, your car begins to back up. You quickly turn the steering wheel, which enables the car to change directions and go forward. You are gaining speed when suddenly you are hit from behind. Your car lurches forward and comes to a stop. You notice that it is your friend who has hit you. You decide to chase your friend. You start to accelerate. Your friend zooms off in the opposite direction. Suddenly, you are heading straight for your friend's car. You accelerate. WHAM! You slam head on, bounce backwards, and stop. You are shaken up. Two more cars run into you, pushing you forward, then backward. You start your car and are moving forward, accelerating toward one of the cars that hit you. Suddenly, the power is turned off and you come to an abrupt stop.

The Jet Fighters

The jet fighters are attached to a central post. Each jet fighter has a tiller that controls the up and down motion of the jet. You enter your jet. The jet takes off slowly, building speed. You pull down on the jet's tiller. The jet climbs, gaining speed. The jets circle with increasing speed. You decide to go into a dive, then climb again. The jet reaches its maximum circular speed. The ride continues for three minutes at this pace. You continue to dive and climb throughout this period. The jets begin to slow their circular motion, and all of the jets descend. It takes one minute for the jets to slow to a stop.

The Roller Coaster

The picture below is of The Big Dipper Roller Coaster. You start out on this roller coaster on the left side of the page and travel from left to right. Sketch three graphs of the ride: time versus distance, time versus speed, and speed versus distance. Explain the ride in terms of speed, acceleration, and deceleration. Describe how you drew the graph and how it relates to the roller coaster tracks.

The Ferris Wheel

You get on a Ferris wheel with 12 cars. Each car has 2 seats. The operator starts and stops the Ferris wheel to allow riders to board and exit the ride. After each ride, the operator lets the riders in every other car exit the ride. After 6 cars of riders board the Ferris wheel, the operator starts the ride and it then turns 12 times at a constant speed. Then the operator lets customers exit the ride in the same manner that they boarded. You are in the third car of riders to exit the ride.

And They're Off!

In this activity, you will participate in a race in which you move your vehicle by using information about direction and speed. To start, each player places his or her vehicle on the starting line by drawing a dot on the track. No two vehicles may occupy the same spot at the same time. Then the players roll a number cube to determine who goes first; the player with the highest number begins and play follows in a clockwise direction. Each vehicle begins with a speed of (0, 0). The goal is to be the first player to reach the finish line without going off the track.

To move your vehicle, start by choosing any two coordinates that will keep your vehicle on the track. The first coordinate indicates movement left and right. A positive number indicates movement to the right while a negative number indicates movement to the left. The second coordinate indicates movement up and down. A positive number indicates movement up while a negative number indicates movement down. You may change the speed and/or direction of your vehicle by adding 1 (+1), subtracting 1 (–1), or adding 0 (+0). For example, suppose your vehicle's current speed is (1, 2) and you want to accelerate its movement to the left and decelerate its movement up to negotiate a turn. You would subtract 1 from the first coordinate and subtract 1 from the second coordinate. Then the new speed of the vehicle would be (0, 1). Use the recording sheet to record your speed after each turn.

Mark each new ordered pair by drawing a circle on the track and then drawing a line from the dot to the circle. On your next turn, color in the circle and plot a new point by drawing a circle at the new coordinate.

Keep in mind that no dot can be drawn on or outside the track. If your vehicle goes out of control and leaves the track, you must go back to the starting line and begin again. The first vehicle to cross the finish line wins.

COMPUTER investigation

The Great Race

In this activity, you will use a computer program to run race cars around a track. You may accelerate, decelerate, turn right, or turn left as you drive around the track.

- To accelerate, press the A key.
- To decelerate or slow down, press the S key.
- To turn right, press the K key.
- To turn left, press the J key.
- To quit or stop the race, press the Q key.

Each time the A key is pressed, the car accelerates. Likewise, the car slows down when the S key is pressed and will come to a complete stop if it is pressed enough times. The car turns 30° every time the J key or the K key is pressed. The car will stay at a constant speed and direction if no key is pressed. If a car goes off the track, the race stops. During the race, the current time, speed, and distance appear at the bottom of the screen.

Conduct several races. The computer will record your results. The program compiles data points as you negotiate your way around the race track. The data recorded are the car's current time, speed, and distance traveled.

Analyze your races. Calculate your total time, average speed, and intervals of acceleration. Chart your findings on graphs. Compare your races with other groups and determine how the race would have looked on the same track. Then summarize your findings in writing.

- Describe your race.
- Analyze the speed of your race car.
- When did you accelerate or decelerate?
- Were you able to maintain a constant speed?
- What was easy and what was difficult about driving the car?
- Explain the process you used to study the motion of your car.

Go for the Gold

You are one of the women's track coaches for the United States Olympic team. Your job is to prepare the athletes for the 1,500-meter race. You decide to analyze races from past Olympic games to better inform yourself of race strategy, runners' speeds, and athletic conditioning. You obtain a videotape of the women's 1,500-meter race from the 1992 Olympic Games. After you and your assistant view the videotape, she makes a table of the race data for you to use. This table is shown in the Data Bank. Your task is to analyze the race. Focus in on at least five of the runners. Determine how far the runners run in a period of time. Use that data to create a graph or series of graphs that show their speeds over time. On the graphs, you may track distance against time, time against speed, or distance against speed to illustrate the motion of the runners and the characteristics of the race. Your graphs may focus on more than one runner. Illustrate intervals of acceleration, deceleration, and speed. Note where runners overtake other runners. Calculate the average speed and rates of acceleration of the runners.

YOUR PRESENTATION

Plan and give an oral group presentation. Use chart paper or poster board to display your graphs and analysis. Include a written explanation of your understanding of distance, time, velocity, and acceleration as they pertain to the race. Describe the characteristics of the race and explain how they are illustrated through the graphs that you drew.

Speed Demon

*Y*ou are a design engineer working for a racing car manufacturer. You have been assigned the task of working with a design crew to build a new race car. Your crew's assignment includes: designing the vehicle, building a prototype, and testing the vehicle for speed, distance, and acceleration capabilities.

YOUR REPORT

After your crew has designed and tested the vehicle, you must produce an individual report that describes the process. The report must include:

- a scale drawing of the vehicle,
- a description of the design process,
- a justification of the tests conducted,
- the data that were compiled from the tests,
- an analysis of the vehicle's traveling speed and acceleration capabilities,
- graphs of the vehicle's performance, and
- a performance summary to be used for advertising purposes.

SELECTION AND REFLECTION

- The mathematical terms **function, speed, velocity, acceleration,** and **deceleration** were used throughout this unit. What do these terms mean? Explain them in your own words.

- Describe the mathematics that you used in this unit.

- What did you learn while studying this unit? Use examples from several of the activities in the unit in your explanation.

- How did you feel about learning about the mathematics of movement? Did you enjoy the experience?

Sunday Drive

The Problem

The Kanazawa family drove from San Diego, California, to Santa Barbara, California. They traveled at an average speed of 65 miles per hour (mph) for 105 miles, until they reached Anaheim. They slowed down to 35 mph for 45 miles, until they reached Thousand Oaks. Then they sped up to 60 mph until they reached Santa Barbara, 50 miles away. How long did it take them to make the trip?

Anaheim
NEXT 7 EXITS

Thousand Oaks
NEXT 8 EXITS

HISTORIC HEART OF SAN DIEGO

Extension What was their average speed for the entire trip, if they did not make any stops?

The Problem

Suppose that every hour of every day, an airplane leaves Los Angeles for New York City and at the same instant, an airplane leaves New York City for Los Angeles. Each flight takes 5 hours. In a single day, how many airplanes originating in New York City will pass airplanes originating in Los Angeles in the air?

Space Shuttle Suppers

The Problem

In the early space flights, scientists learned a great deal about the body's response to prolonged weightlessness. Now, space shuttle astronauts have a carefully planned menu to provide the energy and nutrients they need during space flights. Each evening meal consists of one main dish, one vegetable, and two desserts, and an appetizer is included every other day. There are 10 main dishes, 8 vegetable dishes, 13 desserts, and 3 appetizers available. How many different evening meals can be served?

The Problem

You are a police officer investigating an accident. A car has hit a truck and you are wondering whether or not the car was speeding. You measure the skid marks and they are 1,528 feet long. The speed limit for the road is 45 mph. The chart you normally use for determining braking distances is shown below. As you can see, it has an ink stain on it. Without getting another chart, how can you determine whether the car was speeding?

THE POLICE REPORT

Speed (mph)	Braking Distance (feet)
5	15
10	60
15	135
20	240
50	1,500
55	1,815
60	2,160

Extension About how fast was the car going?

All Gassed Up

The Problem

Jorge and Benita traded in their old car, which averaged 22 miles per gallon, for a new car, on which the EPA sticker stated that it should average 37 miles per gallon. If Jorge and Benita drive about 12,000 miles per year and the cost of gasoline averages $1.20 per gallon in their area, how much should they expect to save on gasoline during the first year that they own their new car?

The Problem

Shelly and Keisha spent the day at Tons O' Fun Amusement Park. After lunch, the girls decided to try some games on the midway before taking a few more rides. They stopped at a dart game booth where each person pays $1.00 to play, and is given five darts to throw at a target like the one shown below. The first person to score exactly 21 points wins a prize. Keisha thought about the game for a minute and announced that she did not think it was possible to win the game. Shelly disagreed and played the game three times, but with no success. Is the game fair? Explain.

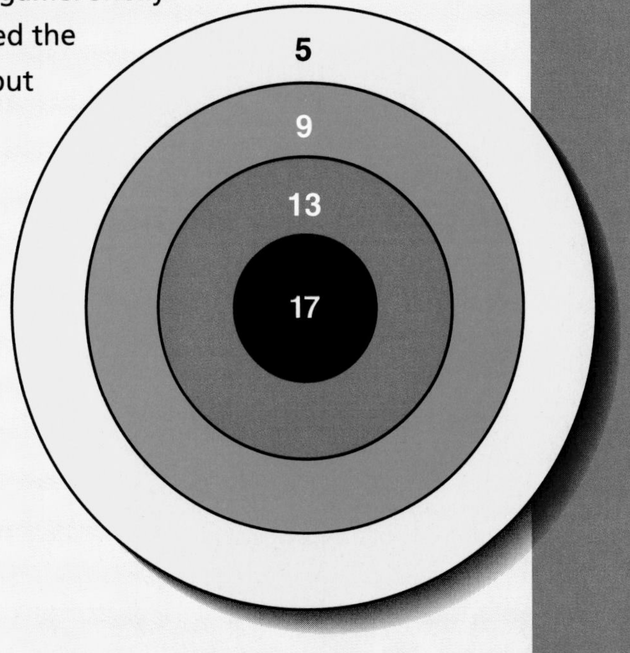

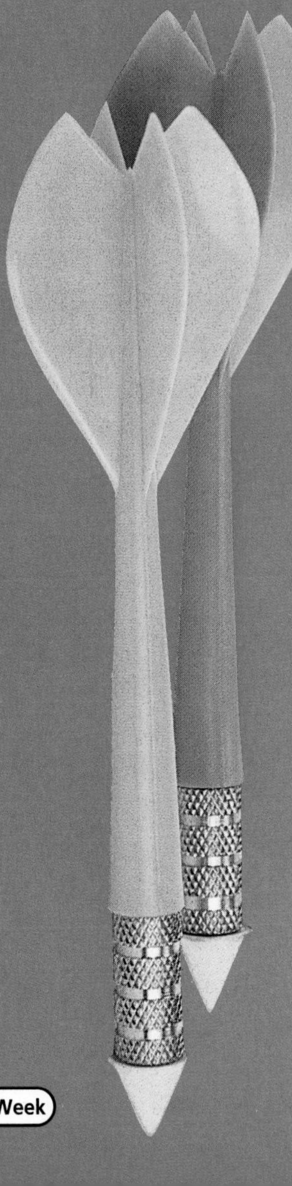

Mischief on the Midway

5

9

13

17

Extension If you determined that the game was fair, write a letter to Keisha explaining why you think so. If you determined that the game was not fair, write a letter to the owner of the amusement park explaining why the game is not fair and how to change the game so that it could be fair.

Blazing a Trail

The Problem

Copy the grid below onto a sheet of paper. Start at the 0 in the top lefthand corner of the grid below and draw a line one square to a 1. Then continue the line two squares to a 2, three squares to a 3, and so on. Make a trail to the 8 in the bottom righthand corner without revisiting any square. You may move horizontally or vertically, but diagonal moves are not allowed.

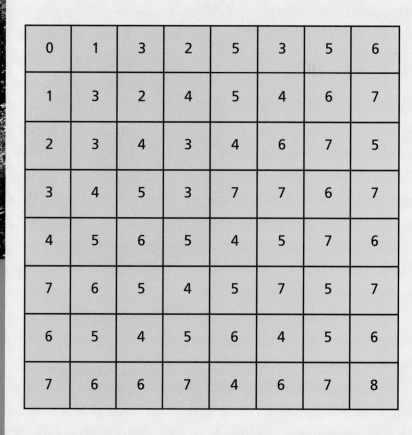

0	1	3	2	5	3	5	6
1	3	2	4	5	4	6	7
2	3	4	3	4	6	7	5
3	4	5	3	7	7	6	7
4	5	6	5	4	5	7	6
7	6	5	4	5	7	5	7
6	5	4	5	6	4	5	6
7	6	6	7	4	6	7	8

TABLE OF CONTENTS

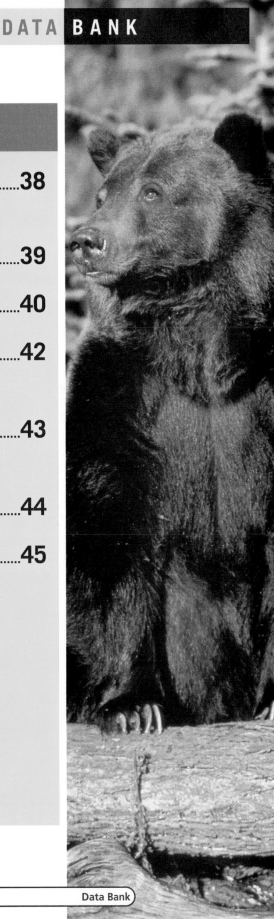

Animal	Speed (mph)	Animal	Speed (mph)
Cheetah	70	Reindeer	32
Pronghorn antelope	61	Giraffe	32
Wildebeest	50	White-tailed deer	30
Lion	50	Grizzly bear	30
Thompson's gazelle	50	Cat (domestic)	30
Quarter horse	47.5	Human	27.9
Elk	45	Elephant	25
Cape hunting dog	45	Black mamba snake	20
Coyote	43	Six-lined race runner	18
Gray fox	42	Wild turkey	15
Hyena	40	Squirrel	12
Zebra	40	Pig (domestic)	11
Greyhound	39.4	Chicken	9
Whippet	35.5	Spider (Tegenaria atrica)	1.2
Rabbit (domestic)	35	Giant tortoise	0.17
Mule deer	35	Three-toed sloth	0.15
Jackal	35	Garden snail	0.03

Source: *1994 Almanac*

24.0-second intervals from launch pad at 0.0 seconds through attainment of orbit at 521.20 seconds

Time (s)	Altitude (ft)	Altitude Rate (ft/s)	Velocity (ft/s)
0.00	0	0	0
24.00	5,718	509	554
48.00	23,417	930	1,101
72.00	50,672	1,419	1,789
96.00	92,282	2,005	3,019
120.00	144,771	2,246	4,102
Solid rocket boosters separation at 125.28 seconds			
125.28	156,483	2,188	4,153
144.00	195,611	1,982	4,438
168.00	239,822	1,704	4,908
192.00	277,429	1,433	5,483
216.00	308,675	1,173	6,154
240.00	333,853	927	6,921
264.00	353,288	695	7,781
288.00	367,351	480	8,739
312.00	376,474	285	9,802
336.00	381,196	114	10,982
Altitude Rate changes from positive to negative at 355.12 seconds			
355.12	382,220	0	11,994
360.00	382,138	−29	12,295
384.00	380,076	−135	13,764
408.00	376,009	−193	15,422
432.00	371,315	−186	17,312
456.00	367,679	−102	19,487
Altitude Rate changes from negative to positive at 473.33 seconds			
473.33	366,731	0	21,120
480.00	366,881	47	21,747
504.00	370,199	246	24,017
Main engines cut off at 521.20 seconds (Thrust = 0)			
521.20	375,636	349	24,950

Source: NASA Johnson Space Center, Houston, Texas

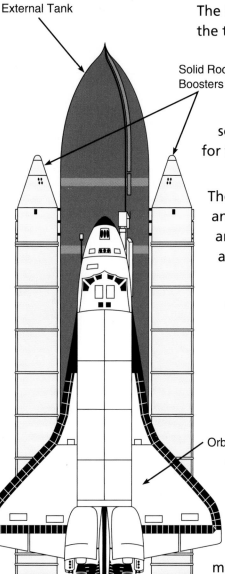

External Tank

Solid Rocket
Boosters

Orbiter

Space Shuttle
Main Engines

The Shuttle's major components are: the orbiter spacecraft; the three main engines, with a combined thrust of almost 1.2 million pounds; the huge external tank (ET) that feeds the liquid hydrogen fuel and liquid oxygen oxidizer to the three main engines; and the two solid rocket boosters (SRBs), with their combined thrust of some 5.8 million pounds, which provide most of the power for the first two minutes of flight.

The SRBs take the Space Shuttle to an altitude of 28 miles and a speed of 3,094 miles per hour before they separate and fall back into the ocean to be retrieved, refurbished, and prepared for another flight.

After the solid rocket boosters are jettisoned, the orbiter's three main engines, fed by the external tank, continue to provide thrust for another six minutes before they are shut down, at which time the giant tank is jettisoned and falls back to Earth, disintegrating in the atmosphere.

The Space Shuttle Orbiter
The orbiter is both the brains and heart of the Space Transportation System. About the same size and weight as a DC-9 aircraft, the orbiter contains the pressurized crew compartment (which can normally carry up to seven crew members), the huge cargo bay, and the three main engines mounted on its aft end.

The thermal tile system that protects the orbiter during its searing reentry through the atmosphere was a breakthrough technology that proved much more challenging than expected. Designed to be used for 100 missions before replacement is necessary, the Shuttle's 24,000 individual tiles are made primarily of pure-sand silicate fibers, mixed with a ceramic binder. Incredibly lightweight, about the density of

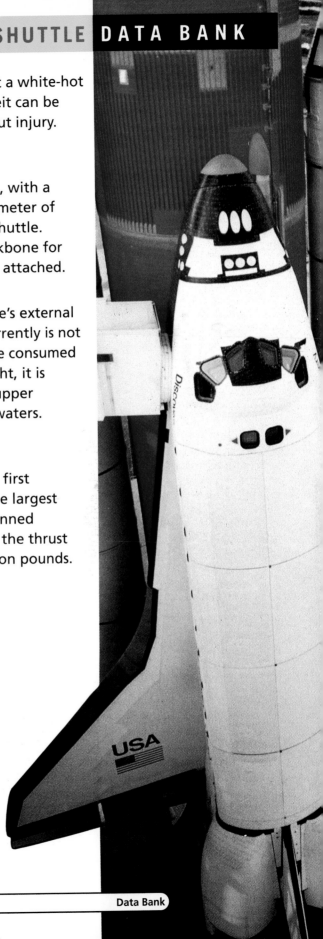

balsa wood, they dissipate the heat so quickly that a white-hot tile with a temperature of 2,300 degrees Fahrenheit can be taken from an oven and held in bare hands without injury.

The External Tank

The giant cylinder, higher than a 15-story building, with a length of 154 feet and as wide as a silo with a diameter of 27.5 feet, is the largest single piece of the Space Shuttle. During launch the external tank also acts as a backbone for the orbiter and solid rocket boosters to which it is attached.

Machined from aluminum alloys, the Space Shuttle's external tank is the only part of the launch vehicle that currently is not reused. After its 526,000 gallons of propellants are consumed during the first eight and one-half minutes of flight, it is jettisoned from the orbiter and breaks up in the upper atmosphere, its pieces falling into remote ocean waters.

The Solid Rocket Boosters

The Space Shuttle's two solid-rocket boosters, the first designed for refurbishment and reuse, are also the largest solids ever built and the first to be flown on a manned spacecraft. Together they provide the majority of the thrust for the first two minutes of flight—some 5.8 million pounds.

Source: NASA Fact Sheet

Kumba, a state-of-the-art coaster at Busch Gardens in Tampa, is a physics professor's dream. Says David Wright of Tidewater Community College, who teaches basic physics by having his students study coasters: "Instead of just reading about the principles of motion and mechanics, students get inside the experiment and experience them."

Gravity

As a poet once said: "The coaster is basically an ornate means of falling." Potential energy is stored in the cars as they are hauled by chain to the top of the 14-story first hill, then released as kinetic energy when gravity pulls them down at 63 mph. Of course, it's not all downhill. Energy sloshes back and forth between kinetic (motion) energy and potential (height) energy. The roller coaster is a fundamentally simple idea—by ride's end, both the energy and the passengers are spent.

Velocity

Though designers have long dreamed of sending riders upside down, their most difficult trick has been a simple loop. Perfect circles, first tried in 1900, required so much velocity that passengers were whiplashed by high centrifugal force. Success finally came in a teardrop-shaped loop, with slower entry and exit speeds but enough force at the tightly radiused top to keep riders in their seats. Still, beneath Kumba's 108-foot-high loop, one can usually find wallets, keys, and hats.

Inertia

On Kumba's double corkscrew, riders go through two stretched-out loops. The track is steeply banked so that centrifugal force will act perpendicular to the seats of the cars, keeping passengers from slamming into one another like bags of groceries sliding across an auto seat during a sharp turn. The banking also diverts the coaster's inertia, its tendency to keep going in the direction it was headed—straight off the track toward Disney World in Orlando, 60 miles away.

Source: *Life* Magazine, August 1988

Order	Name	Country	Time at 400 m	Time at 800 m	Time at 1,200 m	Time at 1,500 m
1	Boulmerka, Hassiba	Algeria	1:00.65	2:05.61	3:09.92	3:55.30
2	Rogacheva, Lyudmila	Unified Tm.	1:00.55	2:05.02	3:09.88	3:56.91
3	Qu, Yunxia	China	1:01.34	2:06.13	3:10.41	3:57.08
4	Dorovskikh, Tatiana	Unified Tm.	1:01.95	2:06.87	3:11.24	3:57.92
5	Liu, Li	China	1:03.64	2:08.91	3:13.76	4:00.20
6	Zuñiga Dominguez, Maite	Spain	1:04.36	2:09.79	3:14.06	4:00.59
7	Rudz, Malgorzata	Poland	1:05.97	2:10.69	3:15.49	4:01.91
8	Podkopayeva, Yekaterina	Unified Tm.	1:04.26	2:10.48	3:16.01	4:02.03
9	Mutola, Maria de Lurdes	Mozambique	1:06.23	2:12.78	3:16.99	4:02.60
10	Plumer, Patti Sue	USA	1:06.19	2:12.59	3:16.42	4:03.42
11	Fidatov, Elena	Romania	1:07.59	2:13.29	3:17.82	4:06.44

Year	Winner	Speed (mph)
1970	Al Unser	155.749
1971	Al Unser	157.735
1972	Mark Donohue	162.962
1973	Gordon Johncock	159.036
1974	Johnny Rutherford	158.589
1975	Bobby Unser	149.213
1976	Johnny Rutherford	148.725
1977	A.J. Foyt	161.331
1978	Al Unser	161.363
1979	Rick Mears	158.899
1980	Johnny Rutherford	142.862
1981	Bobby Unser	139.085
1982	Gordon Johncock	162.026
1983	Tom Sneva	162.117
1984	Rick Mears	163.621
1985	Danny Sullivan	152.982
1986	Bobby Rahal	170.722
1987	Al Unser	162.175
1988	Rick Mears	144.809
1989	Emerson Fitipaldi	167.581
1990	Arie Luyendyk	185.984

Source: *The 1992 World Almanac*

Women's 1,500-Meter Run		
Year	Winner, Country	Time
1972	Lyudmila Bragina, USSR	4 min 1.4 s
1976	Tatyana Kazankina, USSR	4 min 5.5 s
1980	Tatyana Kazankina, USSR	3 min 56.6 s
1984	Gabriella Dorio, Italy	4 min 3.3 s
1988	Paula Ivan, Romania	3 min 54.0 s
1992	Hassiba Boulmerka, Algeria	3 min 55.3 s

Men's 1,500-Meter Run		
Year	Winner, Country	Time
1972	Pekka Vasala, Finland	3 min 36.3 s
1976	John Walker, New Zealand	3 min 39.2 s
1980	Sebastian Coe, Great Britain	3 min 38.4 s
1984	Sebastian Coe, Great Britain	3 min 32.5 s
1988	Peter Rono, Kenya	3 min 36.0 s
1992	Fermin Cacho Ruiz, Spain	3 min 40.1 s

Source: *1994 Almanac*

GLOSSARY INDEX

A

Acceleration, 1, **18**, 19, 22, 23, 24, 25, 26, 28, 29 rate of change in speed intervals of, 27
rates of, 27
Accounting, 2
Adding, 25
Algebra
 axes, 15
 coordinate, 25
 coordinates of an ordered pair, 25
 grid, 36
 horizontal axis, 11, 12, 13, 14, 15
 intervals, 21
 negative number, 25
 plot, 13
 positive number, 25
 vertical axis, 11, 12, 13, 14, 15
Analyze, 20, 21, 22, 26, 27
 data, 1
Average, 6, 19, 34
 speed, 18, 19, 20, 26, 27, 30
Axes, 13, 14, 15

B

Base, 22
Braking distance, 3, 33

C

Calculate, 6, 7, 18, 26, 27
Calculator, 6, 8
Center, 8, 20
Centimeters, 21
Centrifugal force, 42
Change, 1
Charts, 18, 26, 27, 33
Circle, 25, 42

Circumference, 6
Column, 33
Combination, 35
Computer, 2, 26
 program, 26
Coordinates, 25
 of an ordered pair, 25
Count, 15
Cylinder, 41

D

Data, 18, 26, 28
 analyzing, 1
 bank, 18, 27, 37-45
 points, 26
Day, 4, 31, 32, 35
Deceleration, 1, 22, 24, 25, 26, 27, 29
Decimal, 6, 7
Degrees
 Fahrenheit, 41
Density, 41
Diagonal, 36
Diameter, 6, 41
Difference, 33
Direction, 25, 26
Distance, 1, 5, 6, 12, 16, 20, 21, 22, 24, 27, 28
 braking, 3, 33
 stopping, 3
 thinking, 3
Divide, 6, 7

F

Fahrenheit, 41
Feet, 3, 7, 41, 42
Function, 29

G

Geometry
 base, 22
 center, 6, 20
 circle, 25, 42
 circumference, 6
 cylinder, 41
 diameter, 6, 41, 43
 distance, 1, 5, 6, 12, 16, 20, 21, 22, 24, 27, 28
 height, 20
 line, 11, 12, 13, 14, 15, 21, 25, 36
 perpendicular, 42
 point, 13, 14, 15, 21, 25
 square, 36
Graphs, 1, 3, 10, 11, 12, 13, 14, 15, 16, 17, 18, 21, 24, 26, 27, 28
Gravity, 42
Grid, 36

H

Height, 20, 21, 42
Horizontal, 24, 36
 axis, 11, 12, 13, 15
Hours, 6, 7, 8, 9, 31

I

Inches, 8
Inertia, 42
Intervals, 21
 of acceleration, 18, 26, 27

L

Length, 3, 11, 41
Line, 11, 12, 13, 14, 15, 21, 25, 36

PHOTO CREDITS

COVER: John Kelly/The Image Bank;

iii, 1(l), Courtesy of Stephen Lovett, (r), Louis Bencze/AllStock; **2**(t), Courtesy Stephen Lovett, (l), Louis Bencze/AllStock; **3**(t), Scott Cunningham, (screened), Doug Martin, (r), Louis Bencze/All Stock; (cl), file photo, (cr), W. D. Kesler/Photo Resources, (bl), Photoworld/FPG, (bc), file photo, (br), Courtesy Stephen Lovett; **4–5**(b), Index Stock Intl, Inc.; **4**(t)(c)(b), Scott Cunningham; **7**(t), Elaine Comer-Shay, (b), J. Zimmerman/FPG; **8**(l), Todd Yarrington, (r), **9**, K S Studios/Bob Mullenix; **10**(t), Tom Bean/AllStock, (b), G. Robert Bishop/HMS Group/AllStock; **11**(l)(c), K S Studios/Bob Mullenix, (r), Doug Martin; **12**(l), Doug Martin, (r), K S Studios/Bob Mullenix; **13, 14, 15,** Doug Martin; **16**(t), David Ulmer/Stock Boston, (b), Steve Lissau; **17,** Bruce Mathews/Photo Resources; **18,** NASA; **19, 21,** K S Studios/Bob Mullenix; **22**(l), Bob Daemmrich/Stock Boston, (r), Chromosohm/Sohm/AllStock; **23**(l), Aaron Haupt Photography, (r), Jian Chen/Index Stock Intl, Inc; **24,** Aaron Haupt Photography; **25,** Bernard Asset/Agence Vandystadt/Photo Researchers; **26,** Scott Cunningham; **27**(tl), Bill Gallery/Stock Boston, (bl), Don Graham/AllStock, (r), David Madison/DUOMO; **28,** Stacy Pick/Stock Boston; **29**(tr), James W. Kay/Index Stock Intl, Inc., (cr), Photo Sunstar/F-Stock, (bl), Chris Noble/AllStock, (br), Caroline Wood/F-Stock; **30**(tl), Reed Khestner/ Zephyr Pictures, (tr), Tony Freeman/PhotoEdit, (bl), Myrleen Ferguson/PhotoEdit, (br), Reed Khestner/ Zephyr Pictures; **31,** K S Studios/Bob Mullenix; **32,** NASA; **33**(l), Ellis Herwig/Stock Boston, (r), K S Studios/Bob Mullenix; **34,** Doug Martin; **35,** Ken Frick; **36**(t), Aaron Haupt Photography, (b), Larry Hamill; **37,** Alan Carey; **38**(t), Animals Animals/Anup & Manoj Shah, (b), Lynn M. Stone; **39, 41,** NASA; **42,** Paul L. Ruben; **43,** David Madison/DUOMO; **44,** Tom Ebenhoh/Photographic Resources; **45**(l), T. Zimmermann/FPG, (r), Pete Saloutos/Photographic Resources.

ACKNOWLEDGMENTS

40–41, Source: NASA Fact Sheet; **42,** "The Physics of Fear," by George Howe Colt. George Howe Colt, *Life Magazine*, August 1993, pp. 68–71, © Time Warner. Reprinted with permission.